# LOVED BY THE FATHER

## A WOMEN'S BIBLE STUDY AND JOURNAL THROUGH JOHN AND 1ST JOHN

### CAROLYN RICE

Published by Alarias Press,
PO Box 248, Granite Falls WA 98252

Stock Photos purchased from: stock.adobe.com

Credit attribution for Print: Azaliya (Elya Vatel)

Cover Design: Evocative

# PRAISE FOR LOVED BY THE FATHER

I have had the privilege of being Carolyn Rice's pastor. She has written a great book on reading the Bible and journaling. If you read it and follow its instruction you will grow closer to the Lord. God is calling you through this book. Enjoy!

Dr. Dan Hammer
Senior Apostolic Leader
Sonrise Christian Center
Everett, WA

# CONTENTS

# ACKNOWLEDGMENTS

Thank you,

To my husband Lyle. You have always believed I could.

To my home group in Granite Falls, Washington for praying me through this book.

To Doug and Becky for loving us well and being so supportive.

To Pastor Dan, for your encouragement, ideas, and willingness to endorse my book.

To Kerry, Tracy, Dawn and Debbie for reading this book before it was published and giving me feedback.

To Jesus, I give this book to you. You know exactly who will read the words within, and you were thinking of them while I wrote it. May you touch every person in a special way, giving them a picture of the Father's love just for them.

# YOUR FREE GIFT

Have you struggled with rejection, fear, or a broken heart?
Author Carolyn Rice, a survivor of severe abuse, struggled with all
of these and more. There were times she felt alone and isolated, like
the only one who understood at all was God.
*God Sees Your Tears* is a collection of prayers calling out to God for
help with discouragement, anger, shame, bad memories and more.
Each prayer comes with a scripture to find comfort from God's
word.
You don't have to feel alone anymore.
Sign up for Carolyns email newsletter at CarolynsBooks.com and
download your free gift.

**Email Subscribers will:**

- Receive a weekly newsletter from Carolyn
- Be the first to know about new new books and author news
- Receive sneak peeks and be included in drawings exclusively for email subscribers
- Be the first to have an opportunity to become an influencer for future books: which means you receive a free digital or print book in exchange for leaving your honest review on Amazon. Spots for influencers are limited.
- Your email address will never be shared with anyone, and you may unsubscribe at any time.

Subscribe and download your free gift at Carolynsbooks.com

Open my eyes,
that I may see wondrous things from Your law.
Psalm 119:18

# INTRODUCTION

"What part of the Bible should someone read first?" I asked a pastor during a fifteen-minute break at Bible College.

"The book of John, and First John," He answered emphatically, "Because those are about God's love."

I had just started attending Bible College and was not all that literate in the word of God but wanted to be. I was in for a great journey, and a love for the Bible and Bible Study was birthed into my life during that time.

So many people say, "Just read your Bible."

But for someone who has never done it before, or is new at the practice of it, this can be overwhelming. So, I wrote this Bible study/journal where I myself started in the Word of God; the book of John and 1st John, because as my pastor friend said, "These are about God's love for you."

Knowing the Father loves you is the foundation for everything else. My prayer is that you experience Gods' love through the pages that follow.

# HOW TO USE THIS BOOK

Each day you will find a reading from John or 1st John.

Which Bible translation is best? I love the New King James, the NIV and the New Living Translation. But the best translation is one that you are comfortable reading and that you understand. You can go to Biblegateway.com and find many different versions to read online.

When is the best time to read? The time that fits your schedule. Many people read in the morning. But some read during their lunches at work, or when they get home. While my daughter was young, I waited until she went to bed at night, then had my time with God.

After reading the chapter for the day, there are a few questions to stimulate your thinking about what you've just read. Then you'll be asked to pick a scripture from that chapter which stood out to you.

When you've chosen your scripture, sit quietly for a moment and ask the Holy Spirit to make that scripture real to you. Simply say, "Holy Spirit, I pray that you would make this scripture real to me."

The Lord has given us the Holy Spirit as our teacher, guide and helper (See John 16:7, and John 14:16-18).

Think about what that scripture means for your life. Remember to always keep the scripture in context, meaning, be conscious of the scriptures which are around it. What you don't want to do is take a scripture out of the Bible and make it say what *you* want it to say. Always be aware of the context.

If you have questions and want to study that chapter or scripture further, a great site to go to is blueletterbible.org. Pull up any verse and click on the tools button beside it. You will get information on the Greek and Hebrew definitions of Bible words, Bible dictionaries, cross-references and commentaries.

Every Journal entry will close with the question, how does this apply to my life?

James 1:22-25 says, "But be doers of the word, and not hearers only, deceiving yourselves. For if anyone is a hearer of the word and not a doer, he is like a man observing his natural face in a mirror; for he observes himself, goes away, and immediately forgets what kind of man he was. But he who looks into the perfect law of liberty and continues in it and is not a forgetful hearer but a doer of the work, this one will be blessed in what he does."

In light of this verse, you'll think about what you've just read, and ask yourself how you can apply it into your own life today. There is a sample filled out journal entry in the appendix if you would like to see an example.

# WEEKLY JOURNAL SUMMARY

At the end of every seven days, you'll find a weekly journal summary. The last week is shorter due to the length of chapters in the books of John and 1ˢᵗ John.

For the weekly journal summary, take some time to go back and look at your journal entries for the week. There is a space for you to write down what stood out to you the most.

Then, write down how God touched your heart this week. The Bible says to remember the things God has done for you. What better way to remember than writing it down (See Psalm 77:11).

There have been many times I've gone through old journal entries and been reminded of God's goodness to me. Be sure to write down those little things that God does for you, so you can remember them later!

Another question is, what did the thing that touched your heart show you about God's love for you? This will help you become conscious of God's love and to be looking for the ways He reveals Himself to you.

The last thing in the weekly summary is to choose one scripture to memorize from the seven that stood out to you that week. When

God first started dealing with me about memorizing scripture, I was sure I couldn't do it! But the more I have done it the easier it has gotten, and the more truth I now have living in my heart.

I have written out instructions on how I memorize scripture if you need help. You'll find the written instructions and a sample filled out weekly Journal summary in the appendix.

ead: John 1

What does this chapter show you about Jesus?

He made everything,
even the light & the dark
He is the word God

Write out John 1:3 here:

All things were made through
Him and without Him nothing
was made that was made

Write out John 1: 12-13 here:

*But as many as received Him, to them He gave the right to become children of God, to those who believe in His name, who were born, not of blood, nor of the will of the flesh, nor the will of man, but of God*

What does this verse say about you?

*It says I am a child of God.*

What do these verses show you about God's love for you?

*God love me, made me because I believe in Him*

Write out or say a prayer thanking God for His Love for you:

*Thank you God for your great love for me*

What verse Stood out to you in John 1? Write it here:

_All things were made_
_through Him_

Ask the Holy Spirit to make this verse real to you. Wait quietly in God's presence for a moment, then write what's on your heart:

_God created all things_
_to give Him Praise, all_
_humans + animals._

_____

_____

_____

_____

_____

_____

_____

_____

_____

_____

How can you apply this verse to your life?

God made me to love & receive His love, God made me to receive & enjoy good things, to praise Him & give Him glory.

# DAY 2

 ead: John 2

What does this chapter show you about Jesus?

*Jesus is all powerful*
*He can do signs + wonders*

Write out John 2:11 here:

This beginning of signs Jesus did in Cana of Galilee, and manifested His glory; and His disciples believed in Him.

How did you come to Christ?

I met a bus driver while riding on a city bus, he gave me his phone number so I called him and he led me to the Lord, prayed a prayer of repentance

What does this show you about God's love for you?

God knew I needed His Love & need God in my life

Write out a prayer thanking God for calling you into His kingdom:

Thank you Father God for calling me to yourself, and into your kingdom.

What verse in John 2 stood out to you? Write it here:

V 11 - The beginning of signs Jesus did in Cana of Galilee, and manifested His glory, and His disciples believed in Him.

Ask the Holy Spirit to make this verse real to you. Wait quietly in God's presence for a moment, then write what's on your heart:

God has done many signs + wonders and He will do more in the future. God is not done with me yet. God has many signs + wonders to do.

_____
_____
_____
_____
_____
_____
_____
_____
_____
_____
_____
_____

How can you apply this verse to your life?

Jesus can & will do more Signs & Wonders in My life

# DAY 3

ead: John 3

### What does this chapter show you about Jesus?

We can't see the Kingdom
of God unless we are
Spiritually born again

Write John 3:15-16 here:

Whoever believes in Him should not perish but will have eternal life. For God so loved the world that He gave His only begotten Son, that whoever believes in Him should not perish but have everlasting life

What does this show you about God's love for you?

God wants me to believe in Him, He loves me and wants me to be born again + have eternal life

Write John 3:17 here:

For God didn't sent His Son into the world to condemn it, but the world through Him might be saved.

Did Jesus come to condemn you? No

If you have struggled with condemnation you can pray the following prayer:

*Father God, I lay self-condemnation and condemnation from others at your feet right now. I choose not to carry it around anymore. It is your burden and not mine, for you carried it on the cross so I could be free. I invite you to Heal my heart, mind and emotions. Help me to walk completely free of all condemnation. In Jesus name, amen.*

Write John 3:31 here:

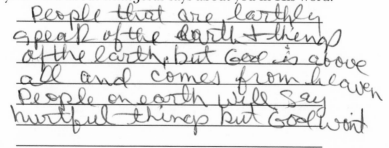

He who comes from above is above all, he who is of earth is earthly and speaks of the earth, He who comes from heaven is above all.

What does this verse say about hurtful words others have said about you? And about what Jesus says about you in His word?

People that are earthly speak of the earth + things of the earth, but God is above all and comes from heaven People on earth will say hurtful things but God won't

What verse in John 3 stood out to you? Write it here:

Some people here on earth
speak hurtful things because
they dont know God but
God is above all.

Ask the Holy Spirit to make this verse real to you. Wait quietly in God's presence for a moment, then write what's on your heart.

How can you apply this verse to your life?

I can hear what God says about me and dont listen + receive the painful or negative things people at work say about me.

# DAY 4

ead: John 4

What does this chapter show you about Jesus?

God will provide for
me when I ask for
it.

Write John 4:29 here:

*Come, See a Man who tole me all things that I ever did. Could this be the Christ?*

Jesus has seen everything you have ever done. He looked at you on your worst day, and He said, "I love you."

Take a moment and thank Jesus for loving you, even in your worst moments.

*Thank you Jesus for Loving me, Even in my worst + Everything I did or didn't do.*

What verse in John 4 stood out to you? Write it here:

*V 23 - The hour is coming, now is when the true worshippers will worship the Father in Spirit + truth, for the Father is seeking such to worship Him*

Ask the Holy Spirit to make this verse real to you. Wait quietly in God's presence for a moment, then write what's on your heart.

God is telling me to be a true worshipper of God worship the Father in spirit & truth.

How can you apply this verse to your life?

God knows everything I have done, even the worst & still says "I love you"

# DAY 5

*R*ead: John 5

What does this chapter show you about Jesus?

He is a Great Healer

Write John 5:17 here:

Jesus got into the boat, went over the sea to word Capernaum It was Already dark, & Jesus had not come to them

Take a moment and thank the Lord that He loves you so much, He
is working in your life today, and that whatever you are struggling
with, He is faithful (See Philippians 1:6).

Thank you Lord for Loving
me and working in my life
I thank you and Praise
you for you are my Faithful
Father

What verse in John 5 stood out to you? Write it here:

John 5:17 - But Jesus
answered them, "My Father
has been working until now
and I have been working"

Ask the Holy Spirit to make this verse real to you. Wait quietly in
God's presence for a moment, then write what's on your heart.

God says, Take heart my
child, I am with you + in
you. "Do not fear" or "worry"
I am taking care of you
and will provide for you
what you need.

_____

_____

_____

_____

_____

_____

_____

_____

_____

_____

_____

_____

How can you apply this verse to your life?

I choose to Believe by
faith, God is with me, he
is in me. He is working
in my life, so I will
thank God & Praise God

_____

_____

## DAY 6

ead: John 6

What does this chapter show you about Jesus?

_____

_____

_____

_____

_____

_____

_____

Write John 6:29 here:

_____

_____

_____

_____

_____

Do you have to work for Jesus to love you?

_____

_____

Write John 6:37 here:

_____

_____

_____

_____

_____

When you come to Jesus, what does this verse say He will never do?

_____

_____

Write John 6:40 here:

_____

_____

_____

_____

_____

According to this verse, what is God's will for you?

_____

_____

_____

What verse in John 6 stood out to you? Write it here:

_____

_____

_____

_____

_____

Ask the Holy Spirit to make this verse real to you. Wait quietly in God's presence for a moment, then write what's on your heart.

_____

_____

_____

_____

_____

_____

_____

_____

_____

_____

_____

_____

_____

_____

_____

_____

_____

_____

_____

_____

_____

_____

_____

_____

How can you apply this verse to your life?

_____

_____

_____

_____

_____

_____

_____

# DAY 7

*R*ead: John 7

What does this chapter show you about Jesus?

_____

_____

_____

_____

_____

_____

_____

Write John 7:27 here:

_____

_____

_____

_____

Read the following Story and think about where you are from, your background, your past sin, or any shame you struggle with. Let God minister to your heart as your read.

Alana's feet were on soft ground. She took a deep, refreshing breath of damp forest. *Such a beautiful place! Why have I never been here before?*

"You've never looked for it."

She whirled around at the voice behind her.

"Welcome to my garden." A bearded man in overalls stood near, smiling with a twinkle in his eyes. "It's one of my favorite places to be."

He took a few steps toward a garden bed, "This is one of my favorite flowers." He pointed to a particular rose. It had sparkles of gold amongst the deep pink.

"It's beautiful." She moved closer and bent to take in the flower's enchanting aroma. She could only describe the smell as pure beauty. She ran her finger across the petals, feeling the silkiness.

"Let me show you where it came from." The man motioned for her to follow him and walked to another garden full of weeds, with a single rose, barely standing up straight among them. The petals were wilted, looking as if they were about to fall to the ground.

"That beautiful rose came from *this* garden?" She looked back at the sparkly rose. She'd much rather be over there.

"There is a great beauty hidden in the most overlooked of flowers. If they were loved and nurtured, their beauty would shine through."

"But that other flower has gold on it. This rose is turning brown!"

"The weeds are starving this flower." He ran his fingers down its crinkled leaves. It stood taller at his touch.

He began to dig it out of the ground, his strong hands

embracing it gently. "People see this flower, and say ugly things about it, even ignore it. That doesn't do the flower any good. But if someone would see that this flower only needs to be nourished, the flower would bud and bloom, until it had a breathtaking beauty." He carried the flower to the other garden.

Alana thought it looked tiny and frail in his hands.

He replanted it, his shovel scraping against the soil as he dug, "So many miss the majesty of this flower, because they only look at what it is, and not at what it could be. It takes a special person to do that."

The man stood up and wiped the dirt from his hands. Kind eyes stared directly into hers. "Do you feel ugly sometimes Alana?"

Alana let her mouth drop open.

Without waiting for her answer, he went on, "You are one of the most precious, beautiful flowers in my garden."

Tears came to Alana's eyes and she brushed them away. She looked up to tell the man thank you.

He was gone.

Have you felt like that wilted flower? Have you felt that that you were too much of a mess to fix? Write out a prayer inviting the Lord to work in you.

_____

_____

_____

_____

_____

_____

_____

Now, write out a declaration that He knows where you are from,
loves you, and is doing a beautiful work in you.

_____

_____

_____

_____

_____

_____

_____

What verse in John 7 stood out to you? Write it here:

_____

_____

_____

_____

_____

Ask the Holy Spirit to make this verse real to you. Wait quietly in
God's presence for a moment, then write what's on your heart.

_____

_____

_____

_____

_____

_____

_____

_____

_____

_____

_____

_____

_____

_____

_____

_____

_____

_____

_____

_____

_____

_____

_____

_____

_____

_____

How can you apply this to your life?

_____

_____

_____

_____

_____

_____

_____

# WEEKLY JOURNAL SUMMARY

*R*ead through your journal entries this week and write down what stood out to you the most.

_____

_____

_____

_____

_____

_____

_____

In what ways did God touch your heart this week?

_____

_____

_____

_____

_____

_____

_____

What does this show you about God's love for you?

_____

_____

_____

_____

_____

_____

_____

Take a moment and thank God for His love for you, and for the things He's done this week.

_____

_____

_____

_____

_____

_____

_____

Out of the entire week of scriptures that stood out to you, which
one will you memorize?

_____

_____

_____

_____

_____

## DAY 8

ead: John 8

What does this chapter show you about Jesus?

_____

_____

_____

_____

_____

_____

_____

Write John 8:6 here:

_____

_____

_____

_____

_____

Write John 8: 11 here:

_____

_____

_____

_____

Have you struggled with other people's accusations and definitions
of you?

_____

_____

If so, you can pray the following prayer:

*Father God, I choose to forgive _____ for his/her accusations and ungodly
definitions of me. Where _____ tried to define me as less than or not
valuable, I ask you Father God, for your healing touch to come into my life. In the
name of Jesus Christ, I take off the false labels, false accusations and wrong
definitions of me now.*
*Satan, I say to you, you will no longer define me. I am defined by my heavenly
Father, and in the name of Jesus I renounce and break every agreement made over
me, by myself or someone else, with false labels, false accusations and ungodly
definitions.*

*I receive my Heavenly Father's love for me and His definition of me. I receive Jesus words for myself, that say, "Neither do I condemn you."*

What verse in John 8 stood out to you? Write it here:

_____

_____

_____

_____

_____

Ask the Holy Spirit to make this verse real to you. Wait quietly in God's presence for a moment, then write what's on your heart.

_____

_____

_____

_____

_____

_____

_____

_____

_____

_____

_____

_____

_____

_____

_____

_____

_____

_____

_____

_____

_____

_____

_____

_____

_____

_____

_____

_____

How can you apply this verse to your life?

_____

_____

_____

_____

_____

# DAY 9

 ead: John 9

What does this Chapter show you about Jesus?

_____

_____

_____

_____

_____

_____

_____

Have the things you've experienced caused you to question God's
love?

_____

_____

_____

_____

_____

_____

_____

If so, you can pray the following prayer with me:

*Father God, I pray in Jesus name that you would place your healing balm on my
eyes, spiritually and physically. Lord, where I have been blind to your love, open
my eyes. Where my vision has been clouded by experience, uncloud my vision.
Where fear has ruled my life, I ask that your love would flow through my veins,
banishing fear from life (1 John 4:18). I pray Father God, that you would
resurrect the dreams and plans that you have for me. Where they have been
muddied, wash them off by the blood of Jesus Christ. May hope come alive
again in me. In Jesus name, Amen*

.

What verse in John 9 stood out to you? Write it here:

_____

_____

_____

_____

_____

Ask the Holy Spirit to make this verse real to you. Wait quietly in God's presence for a moment, then write what's on your heart.

_____

_____

_____

_____

_____

_____

_____

_____

_____

_____

_____

_____

_____

_____

_____

_____

_____

_____

_____

_____

_____

_____

_____

_____

How can you apply this verse to your life?

_____

_____

_____

_____

_____

# DAY 10

ead: John 10

What does this chapter show you about Jesus?

_____

_____

_____

_____

_____

_____

_____

In John 10:7 who does Jesus say He is?

_____

_____

In John 10:9 what does Jesus say you will find if you enter by Him?

_____

_____

In John 10:10 what does Jesus say He came to that you may have?

_____

_____

_____

_____

_____

Write John 10:27-29 here:

_____

_____

_____

_____

_____

_____

What do these verses above speak to you about God's love for you?

_____

_____

_____

_____

_____

What verse in John 10 stood out to you? Write it here:

_____

_____

_____

_____

_____

Ask the Holy Spirit to make this verse real to you. Wait quietly in God's presence for a moment, then write what's on your heart.

_____

_____

_____

_____

_____

_____

_____

_____

_____

_____

_____

_____

_____

_____

_____

_____

_____

_____

_____

_____

_____

_____

_____

How can you apply this verse to your life?

_____

_____

_____

_____

_____

_____

_____

# DAY 11

 ead: John 11

What does this chapter show you about Jesus?

_____

_____

_____

_____

_____

_____

_____

Write John 11:32 here:

_____

_____

_____

_____

_____

Have you ever felt like God wasn't there when something
happened?

_____

_____

_____

_____

_____

_____

In John 11:41, what does Jesus say to the Father?

_____

_____

_____

_____

Ask the Holy Spirit to remind you of a time when God came through. Did He come through instantly, or did you have to wait a little while?

_____

_____

_____

_____

_____

_____

_____

Write out a prayer thanking the Father that He has heard you concerning a situation you are waiting for Him to move in.

_____

_____

_____

_____

_____

_____

_____

_____

_____

_____

_____

_____

_____

_____

_____

_____

_____

_____
_____
_____
_____
_____
_____

What verse in John 11 stood out to you? Write it here:

_____
_____
_____
_____
_____

Ask the Holy Spirit to make this verse real to you. Wait quietly in God's presence for a moment, then write what's on your heart.

_____
_____
_____
_____
_____
_____
_____
_____
_____
_____
_____
_____
_____
_____
_____

_____

_____

_____

_____

_____

_____

_____

_____

_____

_____

_____

_____

How can you apply this verse to your life?

_____

_____

_____

_____

_____

_____

# DAY 12

ead: John 12

What does this chapter show you about Jesus?

_____
_____
_____
_____
_____
_____
_____

Write John 12:16 here:

_____

_____

_____

_____

_____

Write down things in your life that you don't understand, then surrender these things to God while praying the following prayer.

_____

_____

_____

_____

_____

_____

*Father God, I don't understand why these things have happened, or why things are the way they are. But I choose to trust in your love, and that you are faithful (See Hebrews 10:23). I lift these things up to you and surrender them into your hands now. I choose to trust you, and maybe someday, I will understand. In Jesus name, Amen.*

What verse in John 12 stood out to you? Write it here:

_____

_____

_____

_____

_____

Ask the Holy Spirit to make this verse real to you. Wait quietly in God's presence for a moment, then write what's on your heart.

_____

_____

_____

_____

_____

_____

_____

_____

_____

_____

_____

_____

_____

_____

_____

_____

_____

_____

_____

_____

_____

_____

_____

_____

How can you apply this verse to your life?

_____

_____

_____

_____

_____

_____

_____

# DAY 13

 ead: John 13

What does this chapter show you about Jesus?

_____

_____

_____

_____

_____

_____

_____

Write John 13:1 here:

_____
_____
_____
_____
_____

Write John 13:34-35 here:

_____
_____
_____
_____
_____
_____
_____
_____

You can pray the following prayer, asking Jesus to fill you with His love. Then, add to it anything else you'd like to say in the space provided:

*Jesus, I surrender to you every place in my life where I haven't been loved by others and ask you to fill those empty places in me with a heart knowledge of your love.*

_____
_____
_____
_____
_____
_____

What verse in John 13 stood out to you? Write it here:

_____

_____

_____

_____

_____

Ask the Holy Spirit to make this verse real to you. Wait quietly in
God's presence for a moment, then write what's on your heart.

_____

_____

_____

_____

_____

_____

_____

_____

_____

_____

_____

_____

_____

_____

_____

_____

_____

_____

_____

_____

_____

_____

_____

_____

_____

_____

_____

_____

_____

How can you apply this verse to your life?

_____

_____

_____

_____

_____

# DAY 14

$\mathcal{R}$ead: John 14

What does this chapter show you about Jesus?

_____

_____

_____

_____

_____

_____

_____

Write John 14:7 here:

_____

_____

_____

_____

In John 14:9 Jesus says, He who has seen me has seen

_____

_____

Have you struggled with the thought of God being your Father?
Have you had an earthly father who did not give you a picture of
God's love? You can pray and ask God to heal the wounds within
you and give you a picture of a good father.

*Father God, I choose to forgive my earthly father or father figure for hurting me
instead of helping me, for showing me anger instead of love, and for all the ways
he failed me. Father God, help me to see and know what a good father is, heal the
wounds within my heart, and break down the walls around my soul. Break the
barriers that keep me from receiving you as you fully are, a good Father. In Jesus
name, amen.*

Write John 14:21 here:

_____

_____

_____

_____

_____

According to this verse, who are you loved by?

_____

_____

Write John 14:23 here:

_____

_____

_____

_____

_____

What verse in John 14 stood out to you? Write it here:

_____

_____

_____

_____

_____

Ask the Holy Spirit to make this verse real to you. Wait quietly in God's presence for a moment, then write what's on your heart.

_____

_____

_____

_____

_____

_____

_____

_____

_____

_____

_____

_____

_____

———————————————————
———————————————————
———————————————————
———————————————————
———————————————————
———————————————————
———————————————————
———————————————————
———————————————————
———————————————————
———————————————————
———————————————————

How can you apply this to your life?

———————————————————
———————————————————
———————————————————
———————————————————
———————————————————
———————————————————
———————————————————

# WEEKLY JOURNAL SUMMARY

$\mathcal{R}$ead through your journal entries this week and write down what stood out to you the most.

_____

_____

_____

_____

_____

_____

_____

In What ways did God touch your heart this week?

_____
_____
_____
_____
_____
_____
_____

What does this show you about God's love for you?

_____
_____
_____
_____
_____
_____
_____

Take a moment and thank God for His love for you, and for the things He's done this week.

_____
_____
_____
_____
_____
_____

Out of the entire week of scriptures that stood out to you, which one will you memorize?

_____

_____

_____

_____

_____

## DAY 15

ead: John 15

What does this chapter show you about Jesus?

_____

_____

_____

_____

_____

_____

_____

Write John 15:9-10 here:

_____

_____

_____

_____

_____

_____

_____

_____

_____

_____

Write John 15:12 here:

_____

_____

_____

_____

_____

It is sometimes hard to love others, especially when you have not been loved yourself. But you can ask the Father to fill you with love and help you to heal.

_Father God, I pray that you would help me to receive your love for myself, and in turn, give it out to others. Where I have been unloved, rejected, wounded and treated as less than, I pray and ask for your healing touch. Where I have learned not to trust, I pray that you would help me to trust you. I open my heart to you and ask you to do your healing work. Put people in my life who will give me an example of your unfailing love. In Jesus name, amen._

Write John 15:16 here:

_____
_____
_____
_____
_____

What does Jesus say He did in this verse?

_____
_____

So that means you are:

_____
_____

You are loved, and you are chosen. Speak that out loud for a moment.

*I am loved. I am chosen.*

What verse in John 15 stood out to you? Write it here:

_____
_____
_____
_____
_____

Ask the Holy Spirit to make this verse real to you. Wait quietly in
God's presence for a moment, then write what's on your heart.

_____

_____

_____

_____

_____

_____

_____

_____

_____

_____

_____

_____

_____

_____

_____

_____

_____

_____

_____

_____

_____

_____

_____

_____

_____

_____

How can you apply this verse to your life?

_____

_____

_____

_____

_____

_____

_____

# DAY 16

ead: John 16

What does this chapter show you about Jesus?

_____

_____

_____

_____

_____

_____

_____

Write John 16:3 here:

_____

_____

_____

_____

_____

When people hurt you, come against you, or do not love you, why does this verse say this is?

_____

_____

Can you say a prayer for those who have hurt you, that they would truly know the Father?

*Father God, I choose to forgive _____ and I pray that _____ would truly know you as his/her Father. Draw their hearts toward you and help them to experience your love. In Jesus name, amen.*

Write John 16:27 here:

_____

_____

_____

_____

_____

In john 16:32 Jesus says He is not alone because

_____

_____

When you feel alone, picture Jesus sitting right there with you.

What verse in John 16 stood out to you? Write it here:

_____

_____

_____

_____

_____

Ask the Holy Spirit to make this verse real to you. Wait quietly in
God's presence for a moment, then write what's on your heart.

_____

_____

_____

_____

_____

_____

_____

_____

_____

_____

_____

_____

_____

_____

_____

_____

_____

_____

_____

_____

_____

---

---

---

---

---

---

---

How can you apply this verse to your life?

---

---

---

---

---

---

# DAY 17

ead: John 17

What does this chapter show you about Jesus?

_____

_____

_____

_____

_____

_____

_____

In Jesus prayer, who is He praying for in John 17:20?

_____

_____

Are you included in this prayer?

_____

_____


Write down some of the things Jesus prayed for you.

_____

_____

_____

_____

_____

_____

_____

_____

_____

_____

_____

_____


In John 17:23 how does it say the Father loves you?

_____

_____

_____

In John 17:26 what did Jesus pray about God's love?

_____

_____

_____

_____

_____

_____

Write out your own prayer agreeing with the prayer Jesus prayed
for you.

_____

_____

_____

_____

_____

_____

_____

What verse in John 17 stood out to you? Write it here:

_____

_____

_____

_____

Ask the Holy Spirit to make this verse real to you. Wait quietly in God's presence for a moment, then write what's on your heart.

_____

_____

_____

_____

_____

_____

_____

_____

_____

_____

_____

_____

_____

_____

_____

_____

_____

_____

_____

_____

_____

_____

_____

_____

How can you apply this verse to your life?

_____

_____

_____

_____

_____

_____

_____

# DAY 18

ead: John 18

What does this chapter show you about Jesus?

_____

_____

_____

_____

_____

_____

_____

Write john 18:28 here:

_____

_____

_____

_____

_____

The people brought Jesus to be crucified, but did not want to be defiled, so that they could eat the Passover meal. They were only interested in outward appearances and not in their own hearts.

Jesus wants your heart.

If you have lived for outward appearances at any time, you can pray the following prayer asking God to make you more concerned about what's in the heart than what's on the outside.

*Father God, I ask your forgiveness for the times I have been more concerned at times with outward appearances or about what others thought, than about my own heart or the hearts of others. I pray that you would heal me of this. I surrender my heart to you and pray that you would soften the hard places in me with your love. I invite you to come in and do the work you need to do. Circumcise my heart by your spirit (See Romans 2:29). Put a new heart and new spirit in me (See Ezekiel 36:26). In Jesus name, amen.*

What verse in John 18 stood out to you? Write it here:

_____
_____
_____
_____
_____

Ask the Holy Spirit to make this verse real to you. Wait quietly in God's presence for a moment, then write what's on your heart.

_____
_____
_____
_____
_____
_____
_____
_____
_____
_____
_____
_____
_____
_____
_____
_____
_____
_____
_____
_____
_____

How can you apply this to your life?

_____

_____

_____

_____

_____

_____

_____

# DAY 19

 ead: John 19

What does this chapter show you about Jesus?

_____

_____

_____

_____

_____

_____

_____

What did Jesus say in John 19:30?

_____

_____

_____

_____

_____

What does this chapter show you about God's love for you?

_____

_____

_____

_____

_____

_____

_____

What verse in John 19 stood out to you? Write it here:

_____

_____

_____

_____

_____

Ask the Holy Spirit to make this verse real to you. Wait quietly in God's presence for a moment, then write what's on your heart.

_____

_____

_____

_____

_____

_____

_____

_____

_____

_____

_____

_____

_____

_____

_____

_____

_____

_____

_____

_____

_____

_____

_____

_____

_____

How can you apply this verse to your life?

_____

_____

_____

_____

_____

_____

_____

# DAY 20

ead: John 20

What does this chapter show you about Jesus?

_____

_____

_____

_____

_____

_____

_____

Write John 20:27 here:

_____

_____

_____

_____

_____


Have you ever struggled with believing the truth of God's love
for you?

_____

_____


If so, you can ask the Lord to help you fully believe the Lord's love
for you:

_Father God, I ask your forgiveness for not believing fully that you love me. In the
name of Jesus Christ, I plead the blood of Jesus over my mind, memories, and
emotions. I break the power of every lie that comes against the truth of God's
love for me, and I renounce every agreement I have made with those lies. I
command those lies to leave me now, in the name of Jesus Christ._

_Father God, may the truth of your love for me envelope my whole being. Open my
eyes to see how much you love me. In Jesus mighty name I pray, amen._


What verse in John 20 stood out to you? Write it here:

_____

_____

_____

_____

_____

Ask the Holy Spirit to make this verse real to you. Wait quietly in God's presence for a moment, then write what's on your heart.

_____

_____

_____

_____

_____

_____

_____

_____

_____

_____

_____

_____

_____

_____

_____

_____

_____

_____

_____

_____

_____

_____

_____

_____

How can you apply this verse to your life?

_____

_____

_____

_____

_____

_____

_____

# DAY 21

 ead: John 21

What does this chapter show you about Jesus?

_____

_____

_____

_____

_____

_____

_____

Write John 21:22 here:

_____

_____

_____

_____

_____

Yes, but how do you follow Jesus?

First, you spend time with Him. When my husband and I were dating, we had coffee together and talked, almost every day. The more I got to know him, the more I thought about him, and the more he became a part of my heart.

You can get to know Jesus by being in the word of God (See John 1:1), by spending time in prayer (See Psalm 145:18) and through praise and worship (See Psalm 150:6).

Sit quietly in the Lords' presence for a moment and invite the Holy Spirit to speak to your heart regarding following Jesus. Write down the thoughts and impressions that come.

_____

_____

_____

_____

_____

_____

_____

_____

_____

What verse in John 21 stood out to you? Write it here:

_____

_____

_____

_____

_____

Ask the Holy Spirit to make this verse real to you. Wait quietly in God's presence for a moment, then write what's on your heart.

_____

_____

_____

_____

_____

_____

_____

_____

_____

_____

_____

_____

_____

_____

_____

_____

_____

_____

_____

_____

_____

———————————————————
———————————————————
———————————————————
———————————————————
———————————————————
———————————————————
———————————————————

How can you apply this verse to your life?

———————————————————
———————————————————
———————————————————
———————————————————
———————————————————

# WEEKLY JOURNAL SUMMARY

*R*ead through your journal entries this week and write down what stood out to you the most.

---
---
---
---
---
---
---

In what ways did God touch your heart this week?

_____

_____

_____

_____

_____

_____

_____

What does this show you about God's love for you?

_____

_____

_____

_____

_____

_____

_____

Take a moment and thank God for His love for you, and for the
things He's done this week.

_____

_____

_____

_____

_____

_____

_____

Out of the entire week of scriptures that stood out to you, which one will you memorize?

_____

_____

_____

_____

_____

# DAY 22

ead: 1 John 1

What does this chapter show you about Jesus?

_____
_____
_____
_____
_____
_____
_____

Write 1 John 1:3 here:

_____

_____

_____

_____

_____

Who is our fellowship with?

_____

_____

Write 1 John 1:5 here:

_____

_____

_____

_____

_____

Write 1 John 1:7 here:

_____

_____

_____

_____

_____

I always wondered what walking in the light meant, until my theology class in Bible College. The 93 year old instructor told us walking in the light meant walking according to God's word. He shared with us many of his life experiences with the word of God.

Write 1 John 1:9 here:

_____

_____

_____

_____

_____

What is your part in this verse?

_____

_____

What is God's part?

_____

_____

What verse in 1 John 1 stood out to you? Write it here:

_____

_____

_____

_____

_____

Ask the Holy Spirit to make this verse real to you. Wait quietly in God's presence for a moment, then write what's on your heart.

_____

_____

_____

_____

_____

_____

_____

_____

_____

_____

_____

_____

_____

_____

_____

_____

_____

_____

_____

_____

_____

_____

_____

_____

How can you apply this verse to your life?

_____

_____

_____

_____

_____

_____

_____

# DAY 23

 ead: 1 John 2

What does this chapter show you about Jesus?

_____

_____

_____

_____

_____

_____

_____

According to 1 John 2:3 how do we know that we know Him?

_____

_____

_____

_____

_____

Write 1 John 2:5 here:

_____

_____

_____

_____

_____

How do we know that we are in Him?

_____

_____

Read 1 john 2:9-11 again.
Who is in the darkness?

_____

_____

In verse 11 there are three things mentioned about the one who
hates and darkness. What are they?

_____

_____

_____

_____

Have you struggled with hatred? You can ask Your Heavenly Father to take it from you.

*Father God, I confess that I have struggled with hatred. I repent before you now, and I choose to forgive the one whom I have hated. I ask Father, that you would take this hatred from me, and that your light would shine in the dark places of my heart. Bring your healing and deliver me from all hatred now. In Jesus name, amen.*

What verse in 1 John 2 stood out to you? Write it here:

_____

_____

_____

_____

_____

Ask the Holy Spirit to make this verse real to you. Wait quietly in God's presence for a moment, then write what's on your heart.

_____

_____

_____

_____

_____

_____

_____

_____

_____

_____

_____

_____

_____

_____

_____

_____

_____

_____

_____

_____

_____

How can you apply this verse to your life?

_____

_____

_____

_____

_____

_____

# DAY 24

ead: 1 John 3

What does this chapter show you about Jesus?

_____

_____

_____

_____

_____

_____

_____

Write 1 John 3:1-2 here:

_____

_____

_____

_____

_____

_____

_____

_____

According to this verse, who are you?

_____

_____

In 1 John 3:16 how do you know love?

_____

_____

_____

_____

Write 1 John 3:23 here:

_____

_____

_____

_____

What is His commandment?

_____
_____
_____
_____
_____

In 1 John 3:24 how do you know that you abide in Him?

_____
_____
_____

What verse in 1 John 3 stood out to you? Write it here:

_____
_____
_____
_____
_____

Ask the Holy Spirit to make this verse real to you. Wait quietly in
God's presence for a moment, then write what's on your heart.

_____
_____
_____
_____
_____
_____
_____
_____
_____

_____
_____
_____
_____
_____
_____
_____
_____
_____
_____
_____
_____
_____
_____
_____
_____

How can you apply this verse to your life?

_____
_____
_____
_____
_____
_____

# DAY 25

ead: 1 John 4

What does this chapter show you about Jesus?

_____

_____

_____

_____

_____

_____

_____

What does 1 John 4:10 say about love?

_____

_____

_____

_____

_____

What does 1 John 4:12 say about love?

_____

_____

_____

_____

_____

What does 1 John 4:16 say about love?

_____

_____

_____

_____

_____

What does 1 John 4:18 say about love?

_____

_____

_____

_____

_____

What does 1 John 4:19 say about love?

_____

_____

_____

_____

_____

What verse in 1 John 4 stood out to you? Write it here:

_____

_____

_____

_____

_____

Ask the Holy Spirit to make this verse real to you. Wait quietly in God's presence for a moment, then write what's on your heart.

_____

_____

_____

_____

_____

_____

_____

_____

_____

_____

_____

_____

_____

_____

_____

_____

_____

_____

_____

_____

_____

_____

_____

_____

_____

_____

How can you apply this verse to your life?

_____

_____

_____

_____

_____

_____

_____

# DAY 26

ead: 1 John 5

What does this chapter show you about Jesus?

_____

_____

_____

_____

_____

_____

_____

Write 1 John 5:1 here:

_____

_____

_____

_____

_____

What does this verse say you are if you believe Jesus is the Christ?

_____

_____

_____

Write 1 John 5:2-3 here:

_____

_____

_____

_____

_____

_____

_____

_____

How do you know that you are walking in love?

_____

_____

_____

Write 1 John 5:4 here:

_____
_____
_____
_____
_____

What verse in 1 John 5 stood out to you? Write it here:

_____
_____
_____
_____
_____

Ask the Holy Spirit to make this verse real to you. Wait quietly in God's presence for a moment, then write what's on your heart.

_____
_____
_____
_____
_____
_____
_____
_____
_____
_____
_____
_____
_____
_____

_____

_____

_____

_____

_____

_____

_____

_____

_____

_____

_____

_____

_____

How can you apply this verse to your life?

_____

_____

_____

_____

_____

_____

# WEEKLY JOURNAL SUMMARY

*R*ead through your journal entries this week and write down what stood out to you the most.

———————————————————————
———————————————————————
———————————————————————
———————————————————————
———————————————————————
———————————————————————
———————————————————————

In what ways did God touch your heart this week?

_____

_____

_____

_____

_____

_____

_____

What does this show you about God's love for you?

_____

_____

_____

_____

_____

_____

_____

Take a moment and thank God for His love for you, and for the
things He's done this week.

_____

_____

_____

_____

_____

_____

Out of the entire week of scriptures that stood out to you, which
one will you memorize?

_____

_____

_____

_____

_____

# DID YOU LOVE THIS BOOK?

Please leave a review on Amazon.com

# SIGN UP FOR CAROLYN'S NEWSLETTER

Have you struggled with rejection, fear, or a broken heart?
Author Carolyn Rice, a survivor of severe abuse, struggled with all
of these and more. There were times she felt alone and isolated, like
the only one who understood at all was God.
*God Sees Your Tears* is a collection of prayers calling out to God for
help with discouragement, anger, shame, bad memories and more.
Each prayer comes with a scripture to find comfort from God's
word.
You don't have to feel alone anymore.
Sign up for Carolyns email newsletter at CarolynsBooks.com and
download your free gift.

**Email Subscribers will:**

- Receive a weekly newsletter from Carolyn
- Be the first to know about new new books and author news
- Receive sneak peeks and be included in drawings exclusively for email subscribers
- Be the first to have an opportunity to become an influencer for future books: which means you receive a free digital or print book in exchange for leaving your honest review on Amazon. Spots for influencers are limited.
- Your email address will never be shared with anyone, and you may unsubscribe at any time.

Subscribe and download your free gift at Carolynsbooks.com

# ABOUT THE AUTHOR

Carolyn Rice holds an Associate Degree from Seattle Bible College. She has served in women's ministry, Alpha Ministries, home group ministry, prayer ministry and taught Cleansing Stream Seminars.

She has two grown children and a granddaughter, and lives with her husband and two Boxer dogs in Granite Falls, Washington.

Find out more about Carolyn and her books at Carolynsbooks.com.

# APPENDIX

# EXAMPLE JOURNAL ENTRY FROM 1ST JOHN 1

Read: First John 1

### What does this chapter show you about Jesus?
This chapter shows that God gave His Son Jesus as a way for me to be forgiven of my sins, and that through Jesus I have fellowship with the Father and the Son.

### Write 1 John 1:3 here:
That which we have seen and heard we declare to you, that you also may have fellowship with us; and truly our fellowship is with the father and with his son, Jesus Christ.

### Who is our fellowship with?
The Father and His son, Jesus Christ.

### Write 1 John 1:5 here:
This is the message that we have heard from Him and declare to you, that God is light and in Him is no darkness at all.

**Write 1 John 1:7 here:**

But if we walk in the light as He is in the light, we have fellowship with one another, and the blood of Jesus Christ His Son cleanses us from all sin.

I always wondered what walking in the light meant, until my theology class in Bible College, where the instructor told us walking in the light meant walking according to God's word.

**Write 1 John 1:9 here:**

If we confess our sins, He is faithful and just to forgive us our sins and to cleanse us from all unrighteousness.

**What is your part in this verse?**

To confess my sins.

**What is God's part?**

To forgive my sins and cleanse me from all unrighteousness.

**What verse in 1 John 1 stood out to you? Write it here:**

1 John 1:5 This is the message which we have heard from Him and declare to you, that God is light and in Him is no darkness at all.

**Ask the Holy Spirit to make this verse real to you. Wait quietly in God's presence for a moment, then write what's on your heart.**

The comfort that I myself receive from God, I can share with others. There are people whose lives I can touch with what God has done in my life.

I am still receiving His comfort every day that I spend in scripture and in prayer, and in those times of fellowship with the Father through Jesus Christ, He fills me up with more that I need for that day, and more to give out to others.

God is light. In Him is no darkness at all. Growing up I learned that adults were not safe, but angry and wanted to hurt me. I learned I couldn't trust them. But God is not mad at me. He is a good God, and the darkness does not come from Him. He is the one who provides the way out.

My Heavenly Father desires fellowship with me, wants to comfort me and bring me out of darkness, and will give me opportunities to share the comfort He has given to me with others.

I receive his light, but then I am also a light in this world.

**How can you apply this verse to your life?**

There is a person I met who could use some moral support, and by comforting her with the comfort I received I can show her a little bit more of Jesus in this world.

# EXAMPLE WEEKLY JOURNAL SUMMARY

**Read through your journal entries this week and write down what stood out to you the most.**

God did not choose to just leave me in darkness, He wanted me to be free, and He provided a way out of the darkness. He's not angry, and He didn't just decide to leave me there. He chose to rescue me from darkness. He counted me of enough value to save.

**In what ways did God touch your heart this week?**
During the message of the sermon on Sunday, God gave me a feeling about something, and later, while talking to my husband, God had given him the same feeling. God cared enough about us both to give us the same message about something in our lives.

**What does this show you about God's love for you?**
God did something He could only do and worked things out the way only He could work them out. And I found myself sitting in a situation, where I was reminded of His promises and realized I was sitting there that day, and His promise was coming to pass. God

loves me so much He kept His promise to me and He is working on my behalf in this situation.

**Take a moment and thank God for His love for you, and for the things He's done this week.**

Thank you, Jesus, for loving me so much that you worked that situation in only a way that you could. Thank you for speaking to my heart and my husband's heart on the same subject. Thank you, Father, that you love me enough to want to spend time with me and give me comfort and wisdom, and that you are so good to me.

**Out of the entire week of scriptures that stood out to you, which one will you memorize?**

1 John 1:5 This is the message which we have heard from Him and declare to you, that God is light and in Him is no darkness at all.

# HOW TO MEMORIZE SCRIPTURE

**Suppose you are going to memorize 1 john 1:9.**

From the beginning to the first comma, it says:

*If we confess our sins,*

Repeat that little phrase ten times. Count it on your fingers. Try not to look at it as you say it.

It's ok if you have to look the first couple of times, you will get it.

**The second part of the verse says:**

*He is faithful and just to forgive us our sins*

Now add that to the first part.

*If we confess our sins, He is faithful and just to forgive us our sins*

And practice it ten times, counting it on your fingers and trying not to look.

**The third part says:**

*And to cleanse us from all unrighteousness.*

So now you are going to add that to the rest of what you've just said, repeating it ten times, counting on your fingers and trying not to look.

*If we confess our sins, He is faithful and just to forgive us our sins and to cleanse us from all unrighteousness.*

Can you repeat the whole thing without looking?

Throughout the day, think of that verse and repeat it to yourself.

### Review It

The next day, practice repeating your verse again. This should take less than five minutes. It's ok if you have to peek for the first few days. If you continue to practice, soon you will have it memorized!

## OTHER BOOKS BY CAROLYN

Lord I'm Broken: Devotions on Healing from Abuse

Made in the USA
Monee, IL
01 March 2020